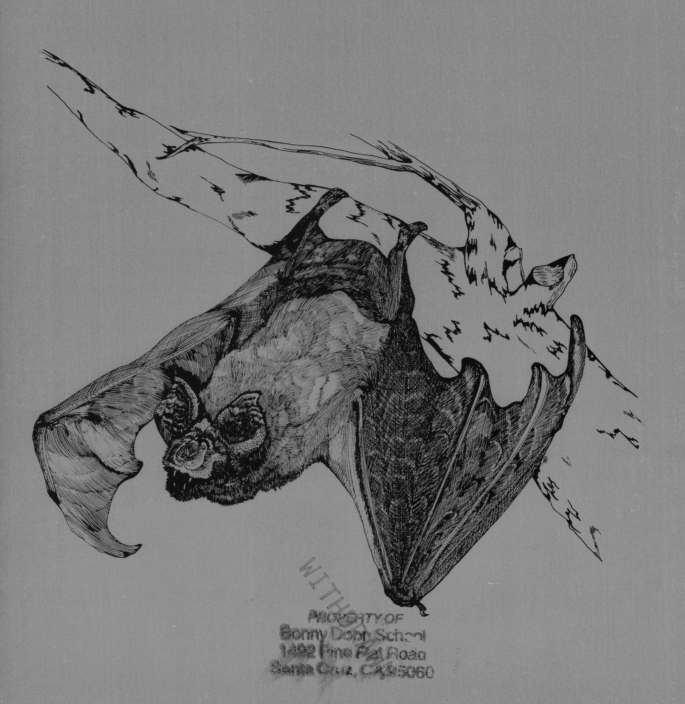

DRACULA

Illustrated by
Greg Hildebrandt

Adapted from the novel by
Bram Stoker

BARNES
&NOBLE
BOOKS
NEW YORK

DRACULA

There are some things born of this world that are so evil, so foul, so wicked—they simply defy imagination. I, Jonathan Harker, have known such evil. I have felt its icy touch. I have choked on its awful breath. I have seen its wicked desire. Its thirst for pain—for power—for blood. I have known such evil. I have known Count Dracula.

But that spring, when I left London to travel to Eastern Europe, I knew only happiness. I was young and in love. I had a good job as an assistant solicitor, and been given a great opportunity to handle the transfer of an estate from Europe to England of a wealthy Count. The Count was from a small country known as Transylvania, which lies in the midst of the Carpathian mountains. Through letters the Count had directed me to purchase a castle outside London, as well as certain furnishings he desired. Having done as he requested, I set off for Transylvania to help him make final preparations for his departure to England. I was engaged to be married to the most beautiful and thoughtful creature ever born—my dear Mina. I thought it best though to wait till my return, not knowing how long I would be away.

The journey was hard. I took a boat from England to France, and then went by train through Europe. Upon reaching Transylvania, however, horse and carriage was the only transportation through the mountains. I should have sensed then from those sinister peaks the danger that awaited me. But I did not. When the Count greeted me at his castle door my only thought was a swift return home—to Mina.

"Count Dracula?" I asked with a polite bow.

"I am Dracula; and I bid you welcome, Mr. Harker, to my house. Come in; the night air is cold, and you must need to eat and rest."

The Count took up my bags, and though they were quite heavy, he handled them as if they weighed not a single pound. He showed me into a great dining hall where an inviting fire was lit. A feast was spread out before me on the table, and the Count offered me a seat by the fire and begged that I eat. For himself, he said he had eaten earlier. There seemed a strange stillness over everything; but as I ate I heard off in the valley the howling of many wolves.

"Listen to them," the Count said, "*the children of the night. What music they make!*" Seeing that I had finished my supper, he said, "You must be tired. Your bedroom is all ready, and to-morrow you shall sleep as late as you like. I have to be away till afternoon; so sleep and dream well!"

But my sleep was anything but pleasant. I suffered strange and nightmarish dreams throughout the night. When I awoke I was in a sea of wonder. I doubted; I feared; I thought such strange things which I dared not confess to my own soul.

The sun was sinking low when the Count came to my room. I did not hear him enter. I was shaving when suddenly I heard behind me, "Good evening." I was startled, and cut my cheek. Looking up in the mirror, I saw no one. I turned half round and saw the Count standing behind me. I turned to the mirror again. He wasn't there! The Count had no reflection! When the Count saw my face, his eyes blazed with a sort of demoniac fury, and he suddenly made a grab for my throat. I drew away and he touched the chain of my crucifix. An instant change came over him.

"Take care," he said, "take care not to cut yourself. It is more dangerous than you think in this country." Then seizing the mirror, he went on, "And this is the wretched thing that has done

the mischief. It is a foul bauble of man's vanity. Away with it!"
And he opened the window with one wrench of his terrible
hand and flung it out to shatter in the courtyard below.

We spent the next two days going over his deed and papers to
the London property and making arrangements for his passage.
My fear grew by the hour and I longed for escape. The Count
had warned me not to venture out of the west wing—as some
harm might befall me. I did wander through the castle, though,
and found that all the doors out were barred and locked. There
was no escape! What terrors this madman held for me, I shuddered to think! It was by chance that I came to know the full
peril I was in.

One evening, after the Count had left me, I began to check
the windows of the castle to see if I might venture an escape by
that route. I was dismayed to find the walls too sheer and high
for any man to climb down. Or so I thought. As I spied out a
window I saw the Count emerge from a window across the way.
With repulsion I saw him begin to crawl down the castle wall,
face down, with his cloak spread out like great wings. He moved
with ease down the sheer, worn wall, just like a lizard moves.

What manner of man was this, or what manner of creature
hiding in the image of a man? I felt the dread of the horrible
place overpowering me. I knew my work for him was almost
done. When he didn't need my services any longer—what then?
I grew desperate to escape and set off through the castle with
only that one end in mind. I frantically ran from one door to
another trying each lock only to find it secure. I soon found
myself on the far side of the castle—a place rank with dust and
age. I was exhausted and running out of hope when at last I
found a door that opened. Entering, I soon discovered it would
offer no escape. It led into a great room—dark and damp and
misty. I suddenly felt the need for sleep overpower me. Before I
knew what I was doing, I laid down, and was fast asleep.

When I awoke, it was as if in a dream. Before me I saw three young women. They whispered together, and laughed—a laughter that sounded silvery and musical.

"Go on! You are first, and we shall follow," one said.

"He is young and strong; there are kisses for us all," said another as she advanced toward me. I was unable to move or speak as she bent over me, licking her lips like an animal. Her head went to my neck. I could feel the soft, shivering touch of her lips on the skin of my throat, and the hard dents of two sharp teeth, just touching and pausing there. I waited with a beating heart.

But at that instant I became aware that the Count was present. He stormed in and grabbed the girl up, tossing her aside with demonic fury. His eyes blazed like the fire from the pit.

"How dare you touch him, any of you? How dare you cast eyes on him when I have forbidden it? Back, I tell you all! This man belongs to me! Beware, or you'll have to deal with me."

"You yourself *never* loved; you *never* love!" said one girl, and the three joined in a hard, soulless laughter. The Count turned and looked at my face attentively, saying in a soft whisper:

"Yes, I too can love; you yourselves can tell it from the past. Is it not so? Well, I promise you that when I am done with him you shall kiss him at your will. Now go! I must awaken him, for there is work to be done."

"Are we to have nothing tonight?" said one of them, with a low laugh.

"Do not fear, I have brought something for you," said the Count, throwing a bag on the floor between them.

The horror overcame me and I sank into unconscious.

When I awoke again, I was back in my room. I shivered with fear at the thought those women were somewhere in the castle waiting to suck my blood. And the Count—what of him? It was daylight, so I knew the Count would be away. I was determined to escape and set off again through the castle. I made my way

down into the lower reaches of the castle where I found a great door. I was sure this would lead to my delivery, so I grabbed up a heavy chair and began pounding it with wild fury against the door. Just as my strength was about to fail me, the lock gave way.

I found myself in a small chamber, full of chests—and these chests were full of gold! I quickly gathered up a handful of coins, knowing that I would need money for my journey, and then proceeded down a narrow passage at the other end of the chamber. There, to my horror, I found where the Count spent his days. In the center of a large and empty hall lay a coffin. Nothing else was could be found in the room. I approached, and drawing a fearful breath, opened it. There lay the Count, with his eyes wide open! I thought for sure he would kill me, but he neither moved nor spoke. I realized then he could not, for whatever reason, move about during the daylight hours. But *his* eyes—those terrible eyes, blazed up at me in demonic anger. He knew I was there. Oh, if only I had had some weapon to rain a fatal blow down upon this vile creature! If I had, others would not have suffered so! But there was nothing in the room to strike him with, so I quickly made my way across the hall, and finding an exit, ran from *Castle Dracula* like a madman.

The next several weeks were unknown to me, as I fell ill with a brain fever at the door of a nunnery and was taken in. There the good sisters tended me. The terror had overcome me, and woe that it did, for the Count made his way to London and I was helpless to follow—helpless to warn the good people of England of the evil that had come amongst them.

What I shall now relate during that time comes from those who suffered most from this accursed creature. The Count made his way by ship to England, hidden within his coffin by day, feasting on the blood of the sailors by night. By the time the ship made port in England, not a man was left alive. Only the captain was found on board, tied to the ship's wheel, with his

throat torn out. The Count had guided the ship along, by what strange power I do not know. Once in port, all arrangements had been made for unloading the Count's things, including fifty coffins full of his native soil! In one lay the Count himself. The coffins were delivered promptly to his new home without anyone knowing what evil lay inside. And without knowing it, I had brought the Beast within the midst of those most dear to me—for I had found him a home right next door to my dear Mina's best friend, Lucy Westenra. At least my Mina was safe for the moment, for the nuns had informed her of my illness, and she came at once to tend me back to health. As for Lucy, the Count wasted no time in satisfying his bloodlust.

Lucy Westenra was, yes was, a beautiful and pure creature. She was engaged to be married to my good and trusted friend, Arthur Goldalming. Count Dracula could somehow hypnotize his victims and call upon them against their will to do his bidding. Helpless, poor Lucy began coming to him at night, and he would feast upon her rich and noble blood as he pleased. The result being that within but two short days Lucy Westenra lay dying from loss of blood.

Near her home was an asylum, where her good friend Dr. Seward oversaw the ill and mentally disturbed. He was sent for at once, for Lucy had been found unconscious in bed that morning by her mother. Dr. Seward was completely baffled. Here lay what should be a perfectly healthy young women, yet her pale face and cold skin told him death was near. He could find no cause for her condition, and nothing seemed out of the ordinary, with the exception of two tiny puncture wounds on the right side of her neck.

He determined he needed help, and wired his friend and colleague, Dr. Van Helsing, in Amsterdam. In the telegram he explained as best he could the symptoms the dying girl exhibited. He awaited Helsing's reply. It was not a wire that Dr. Seward

found at his door the next morning, but Van Helsing himself.

"Professor? You've come?" said the shocked Seward. "I didn't think that would—"

"Ah, my good friend," said Van Helsing, "I know, I know you did not except to see me, but if what I think bears true, your patient is in grave danger of losing her life—and more! We haven't a moment to lose. Please, let me see her at once."

"I don't understand, Professor."

"All will come to light, my friend, but first let's attend to the young woman at once!"

Dr. Seward took Van Helsing immediately to see poor Lucy. Van Helsing examined the pale girl thoroughly, with special attention to the wounds on her neck, then turned to Dr. Seward, saying, "She is ill from loss of blood—a great deal of blood. She will need a transfusion at once or her heart will cease to beat."

"Loss of blood? How? When?" cried Dr. Seward.

"No time for that now. Can I rely on your noble blood to bring her back to life?" Van Helsing asked.

"Of course! I would do anything for this dear lady."

Van Helsing pulled a tube and needle from his bag, and they set to work transferring Dr. Seward's life-giving blood into Lucy's empty veins. In no time the bloom of youth and strength returned to Lucy's cheeks.

"You have done it, Professor," said Dr. Seward.

"Only for the moment, my friend. This young woman is still in very grave danger. I cannot explain now, as you would not believe me, but everything I ask you to do you must if she is to live. We must act swiftly or be lost."

"Willingly, sir! What must we do?"

"First, Miss Lucy must be guarded at all times. She cannot be left alone for one instant. Also, garlic blooms must be placed around her neck and throughout the room. Do these things and wait for my return. There is a great evil behind her illness, and I

must return home to find the answers to overcome it. Wire me every day detailing her condition. I will return shortly and then you shall know what peril we face."

Without another word, Van Helsing left, and Dr. Seward immediately sent for Arthur Goldalming, and an American friend of his, Quincey Morris. He explained to them what must be done, and they vowed to do their utmost. Lucy grew stronger with each passing day, spending most of her time with her beloved Arthur. Dr. Seward wired Van Helsing with the good news, but in reply he would receive a warning not to let their guard down. It was the end of the week when disaster struck.

Arthur's father, Lord Goldalming, died suddenly. Lucy assured him and Quincey that she was fine, and that they could leave at once to make arrangements. After all, she had the good Dr. Seward, her mother, and the servants to watch over her. They agreed, and set off at once.

But Dr. Seward could not come that night. A patient of his, quite mad, by the name of Renfield, went completely berserk. He screamed curses, fought in a frenzy with the orderlies, and called from his window, "Master, Lord, my Lord, come for me!" His cries were directed toward the Count's home.

Lucy's mother, concerned about her daughter's safety, came and slept with her that night. About midnight, they heard something outside the window—a curious scratching sound. The next moment the window came crashing in, and the head of a white wolf, with blazing eyes, came through. The wolf retreated, but Lucy's mother could not bear the terror. Her heart had been weak for many years, and her fright now caused it to fail. She died instantly. In a fit of fear and grief, Lucy ran for the servants. She found them in the kitchen, fast asleep on the floor. They had been drinking sherry, but Lucy could distinctly smell the sleeping drug, laudanum. Who had drugged them? Lucy returned to her mother. There the Count was waiting for her.

When they found her the next morning, she was lying beside her dead mother, ghastly pale and barely breathing. Van Helsing had returned, and after looking at her, said nothing could be done. As Van Helsing and Dr. Seward looked on, poor Lucy gave up her life with one low, sad whimper from her white lips.

Arthur, grief stricken, returned at once. The funerals were held for Lucy and her mother, and they were both entombed in the family mausoleum.

"Poor Arthur!" said Dr. Seward. "He has lost his father, his bride-to-be, and his bride's mother! At least for Lucy, the suffering is now over."

"Oh, if that were only so!" Van Helsing said with a moan; "but, alas, it is not to be. Not yet is there peace for the dead."

"What are you saying? The girl is dead and buried!" said Dr. Seward, shocked by his friend's response.

"There were things I could not tell you before, and though I shall tell you now, you will not believe. But you will be a believer before long. We have holy work to do this very night! The evil that took Miss Lucy's life is *not* dead. Madam Lucy is *not* dead—rather to say she is *Un-Dead*."

"Have you lost your mind, Professor?"

"Not yet, my friend, but before this is over both of us might go mad. How do you account for her death by loss of blood? It did not just disappear, did it? No! It was taken from her—sucked from her sweet body by a fiend. The marks on her neck were the marks of a demon. They are the marks of the vampire. Yes, do not mock me, my friend, for I shall give you proof. Tonight, we must go to the graveyard and see Miss Lucy. She will walk out into the world as the Un-Dead, for she has been bitten by the vampire, and all who have must become as they—creatures of the night. She sleeps now, but tonight she will feed upon the blood of the innocent. We will be waiting, and God willing, we will bring rest and peace to her tortured soul!"

Though in great doubt, Dr. Seward agreed to go with his friend. Arthur and Quincey came too, though nothing of vampires was said to them, only that it was important they should come. They hid themselves behind tombstones just outside the mausoleum and waited. Just before dawn, though all were in shock and disbelief, none stood in doubt. She moved like a ghost through the graveyard, her white death dress flittering in and out between the tombstones. Van Helsing stepped out and barred her way to the tomb. He brought forth a lantern and a cross, stopping her just outside the entrance. It was Lucy Westenra, but yet how changed. Arthur began to step forward, but stopped dead in his tracks with a shudder of horror. Van Helsing raised his lantern and the light fell on Lucy's face. Her lips were crimson with fresh blood, and a stream of blood trickled over her chin and stained the purity of her death-robe. Her eyes blazed up at Van Helsing and she howled like a demon. Dr. Seward grabbed Arthur and made him stand back. She howled again, and then rushed for the tomb door. Van Helsing let her go, as he knew he had to prepare the others for what they must do.

"I am so sorry you had to see your beloved so," he said to the grieving Arthur; "but it was necessary that you see the wickedness with your own eyes, all of you, if you were to believe. Now that you have seen this creature that looks like your dear Lucy, but is not, I will explain the brave work that must be done."

Van Helsing told Arthur and Quincey what he had already told Dr. Seward about vampires. Then he said:

"The vampire is weak by day and must lay in wait for sundown before venturing out into the world. It is at this time, between sunrise and sundown, that the vampire is vulnerable. We must strike, and strike bravely, if we are to release Miss Lucy's soul."

"Whatever is to be done," said Arthur, "allow me, Professor to do it. She was my love, and would have been my wife. I will not

fail you. I will not fail her."

"Yes, yes, you have a brave heart young man," said Van Helsing as he placed a hand on his shoulder. "You will strike boldly for love's sake. For love's sake you shall free her!" And from a bag he drew out a hammer and a sharp wooden stake. "Yes, you will strike. Come, I will show what must be done."

The sun was just rising as they entered the tomb. Van Helsing opened Lucy's coffin and gave the hammer and stake to Arthur.

"All right," said Arthur hoarsely, drawing in a deep breath. "Tell me what I am to do."

"Take this stake in your left hand, place it over her heart, and take the hammer in your right hand. Then when we begin our prayer for the dead, strike in God's name, so all may be well with the dead and that the Un-Dead may pass away."

Arthur took up the stake and hammer, and when once his mind was set on action his hands never trembled. Van Helsing began to read the prayer, and Arthur placed the point over her heart. Then he struck with all his might.

The Thing in the coffin writhed; and a blood-curdling scream came from the open lips. Her sharp white teeth clamped down in agony, and her eyes flashed with misery and pain. But Arthur never faltered. His face was set, and high duty shined through it as he drove the stake deeper and deeper. As the stake pierced the heart, the screaming stopped, and a change came over her face. She once again looked her sweet, pure self. She called out in a choked voice:

"Arthur? Oh, my love—*my dear love*." And then she lay still.

Arthur turned away and dropped the hammer. He uttered such a cry of grief and pain that all shuddered at the sound.

"She is no longer a grinning devil—a foul Thing of the night," Van Helsing said. "No longer is she the devil's Un-Dead. She is God's true dead, whose soul is with Him! Now, my friends, we must find and destroy the author of this evil!"

I returned to England shortly after these terrible events, recovered from my illness and newly married to my beloved Mina. She had not wished to wait till our return, so we were married before leaving Europe. We immediately went to see Dr. Seward upon hearing the news of Lucy's death. My worst fears were confirmed after listening to Professor Van Helsing's account of the events before and after Lucy's death. I informed Van Helsing that the evil that stalked London was Count Dracula, and gave him a detailed account of my stay in Transylvania. Dr. Seward offered his home to us while we figured out what to do about the Count. Mina and I gladly accepted.

The next day Van Helsing called us all together.

"My friends, I have a history on our Count Dracula—I think we should all know what we're up against. He was in life a wonderful man. He drove the Turks from his land and saved his people in a great war. He was a soldier, statesman, and alchemist—that being the science of the time—for this Count lived hundreds of years ago! He had a mighty brain, a learning beyond compare, but he *was* seduced by the Dark Arts, and that is how he came to be a vampire. He has the strength of twenty men, and a cunning more than mortal, for his cunning be the growth of ages. He can direct the elements; the storm, the fog, and the thunder. He can also command all the meaner things: the rat, the owl, the bat, the moth, the fox, and the wolf. He himself can take the shape of the bat or the wolf. At times he has been known to vanish completely, or become but a mist that can slide silently even through a keyhole to reach his victim. He is noneother than the Father of his race—the race of vampires. He must be destroyed!"

"Destroyed!" I cried. "How can we possibly destroy that?"

"We must have faith in ourselves and trust to God," said Van Helsing. "We can start by destroying the coffins, fifty you say, that he has brought with him. He will have no rest from us!"

We made a plan for the destruction of the coffins. It wasn't easy, but I discovered through contacts in London that the Count, upon his arrival, had brought numerous houses all over the city. The fiend! With safe havens throughout the city he could strike at will wherever he pleased. We set out in groups to each house, and when once a coffin was discovered, we placed a Sacred Wafer in the soil within the coffin, thus making it hallowed earth, and death to the vampire if he should lie upon it.

Before the week was done, all but one coffin had been found and rendered useless to the Count. Oh, how foolish we were though! While we were out seeking his destruction, he was feeding nightly! And it was not some poor soul caught out in the streets too late: he was draining the life out of my Mina! I had been so busy scouring the city for Dracula's lairs that I hadn't even noticed what was happening in my own bed! Mina had been restless, yes, and quite pale, but we both put that down to the death of Lucy and the stress of having this monster in our midst. I thought she was safe in Dr. Seward's house, for Van Helsing had told us that a vampire cannot cross the threshold of a home unless he is first invited to enter. Then who invited Dracula into the house? The answer was not long in coming.

It was Dr. Seward's patient, Renfield. The asylum was attached directly to the house. The Count promised Renfield immortality if he would invite him in. The Count's nightly visits continued for a week until Renfield finally understood where he was going. Renfield had been visited by my wife, and being the sweet and pure creature she is, he was quite affected by her. So when the Count appeared shortly after midnight in his cell, Renfield tried to stop him from hurting Mina. It cost him his life. The Count grabbed and lifted him up like a small infant, then hurled him face down on the floor. Renfield's head was crushed. A scream was heard coming from his cell, and Dr. Seward came at once. With his last dying breaths, Renfield told him everything.

"Dracula, here? That devil!" Dr. Seward said to himself. He quickly woke Van Helsing, and together they awakened Quincey and Arthur. Then silently they came to our room. Quincey broke down the door and then stood motionless—frozen with shock and horror as he looked upon the gruesome scene before him.

There on the bed I lay, deep in some hypnotic trance, while the Count stood over my Mina, drinking of her blood. As they burst into the room, Dracula rose from his fiendish work, his eyes flaming red with devilish passion. His sharp white teeth, behind blood-dripping lips, he clamped together like a wild beast. And most remarkable, he now had the appearance of a young man!

"Foolish men!" said the Count. "Do you *really* think you can stand against me! Many have tried—all have died!" Then pointing to Mina, he said, "You are too late! She is *mine* now!"

At those words, Dr. Seward stepped boldly forward and raised a cross up to the Count's face. Dracula fell back in a fit of agony and despair at the sight of the cross. He growled horribly, and then with a wave of his cloak, he was gone! He became but a blue mist and vanished through the window.

Through great effort Van Helsing was able to finally rouse us both from our trances. When we were told what had occurred I was shocked to silence as my poor Mina wept with despair in my arms. Van Helsing took a Sacred Wafer and said a blessing, then placed the wafer on each of our foreheads in turn as a means of holy protection. But when he placed the wafer on Mina's forehead it burned its holy image into her pale skin.

"I am doomed, my love," she cried. "God has marked me! I am unclean!"

Before I could speak, Van Helsing took her by the hand, saying, "Do not fear, my child, it is not too late. We must destroy Count Dracula, of that I am certain. If we succeed, you shall be free and pure once again. If we fail, we shall all perish. *We shall not fail!*"

Mina took courage from the Professor's words, as did I. At first dawn's light we would enter the Count's house and destroy the monster. God willing, this nightmare would end! But come morning, I found it would not be so.

We entered the Count's house at daybreak only to find it empty. The Count had fled in the night! But where could he have gone, I wondered. Had we missed some secret hideaway. Suddenly, Mina touched my shoulder, and said, "Jonathan, I can feel him. Somehow I am bound to him." Then turning to Van Helsing, she continued, "Professor, I know where he is. He is fleeing by boat back to Transylvania—back to Castle Dracula. He delivered his coffin to the ship before sunrise, and is now lying within it until he reaches the castle. Though in darkness, I can hear the lapping of the waves and the creaking of the boat."

"Bless you, child! There is still hope!" proclaimed Van Helsing. "Since he needs to travel by water, it will take him two weeks to reach home. We shall go overland and be waiting for him at Castle Dracula when he arrives! But nothing must be left to chance. Come, let us prepare for the journey at once!"

We took a steamship across the channel the next day, and then proceeded by train to Greece. There it was decided to break up into groups, as the Count would come by boat up one of two rivers that cross near Castle Dracula. Dr. Seward and myself went by boat up one river while Arthur and Quincey followed the bank of the other on horseback. Van Helsing took Mina with him by horse and carriage overland. Mina *was* changing. She now had to sleep the entire day, from sunrise to sunset, and at night, a strange restlessness would come over her. Van Helsing saw that the closer they drew to Castle Dracula, the more restless Mina became. He only prayed the Count could be destroyed before she changed completely—before she too became a vampire! After three days, they arrived just outside the castle grounds. We would not arrive till late the following day. They were alone!

A heavy snow had fallen by the time they made camp for the night. Sensing danger in this desolate place, Van Helsing build a large fire and drew a holy circle in the snow around them. He then crushed Sacred Wafers into a fine powder and poured them along the circle. He had just finished his holy work when they came. The horses began to scream and pull at their tethers. At first they came as a blue mist, but little by little their physical shapes took form. Van Helsing recognized them at once as the vampiresses that I had seen in the castle. They sang out in their silvery voices to Mina, calling, "Come, sister, come with us. Come! Come! You belong with us!"

Van Helsing turned to see Mina's face, and the look of horror on her face reassured him that she was as yet not one of them. He held a Sacred Wafer up to their faces, and the three vampiresses retreated in a mist back to the castle. Van Helsing, sure of the safety of the holy circle that surrounded them, laid down to sleep. He knew he would need his strength for the horrible work he would do come dawn.

As the first rays of dawn spread across the snow-capped mountains, Van Helsing silently left Mina, who was now asleep, and set off for Castle Dracula. Once there, he entered a tomb on the east wing of the castle. Looking among the dead he finally found the three vampiresses, sisters all, as their tombstones revealed. A sadness overcame him as he looked down at the first fair sister. Pity and sorrow was in his heart to see such a beautiful child lying in a tomb with the age and dust of centuries. The moment passed, however, and he remembered his duty, not only to Mina and his friends, but to these children of the night. Their souls must be free! He took stake and hammer in hand, and began his terrible work. He drove a stake deep into the heart of each sister—freeing them forever from the misery of the Count's curse.

Once done, he entered a grand tomb, marked with the word "Dracula" at its entrance. This was the Un-Dead home of the

King-Vampire. Before returning to Mina, Van Helsing laid some Sacred Wafer in Dracula's tomb, and so banished him from it, Un-Dead, forevermore.

When he returned to Mina, he found she was wide awake, though the day was not over.

"Oh, Professor, we *must* hurry!" she pleaded. "The Count is coming and sun will soon be down!"

Mina led the way down a mountain path to the road that went straight to Castle Dracula. Van Helsing, looking off in the distance, could see horsemen approaching, probably gypsies by their appearance. Behind them a cart was being pulled, and in that cart lay the coffin of Dracula. They were riding at break-neck speed, trying themselves to beat the setting of the sun. Though unarmed, Van Helsing was determined to stop them before they reached the castle, and so stepped boldly into the road to block them.

But he was not alone, for at that moment, Arthur and Quincey came into view, riding with wild abandon to overtake the gypsies. And from another side, Dr. Seward and myself appeared, also riding furiously down upon the horsemen. The race was on. Arthur and Quincey overtook them first, calling for them to halt. Arthur had a pistol and Quincey had his bowie knife. But the gypsies did not understand a word of english, and surely must have thought us robbers. They stopped and turned, with knives drawn, and a fight ensued before Dr. Seward and I could reach them with our rifles.

During the fight, Quincey was stabbed in the side. He didn't falter for a moment though, jumping onto the cart which was again racing toward the castle. With superhuman effort, he managed to push the coffin off into the road. We arrived at that moment and raised our rifles at the gypsies, who quickly gave up and stopped. I jumped from my horse as Dr. Seward and Arthur held their guns on them, and joined the injured Quincey at the

coffin. We were both in a panic, for the sun *was* going down! I threw down my rifle and pulled a great Kukri knife from my belt. Quincey and I took our knives and attacked the coffin with desperate energy, attempting to pry off the lid. Under our efforts the lid began to yield; the nails drew with a screeching sound, and the top was thrown back.

The sun was almost down on the mountain tops, and the shadows of the whole group fell long upon the snow. I saw Dracula lying within the box upon the earth, some of which the fall from the cart had scattered over him. He was deathly pale, just like a waxen figure, and the red eyes glared with the horrible look of hate that I knew all too well.

As I looked, his eyes saw the sinking sun, and the look of hate in them turned to triumph.

But, on the instant, came the sweep and flash of my knife into his throat. At the same moment Quincey's knife plunged into his heart.

It was like a miracle—before our very eyes, and almost in the drawing of a breath, Count Dracula crumbled into dust and passed from our sight forever.

I shall always be glad that in that moment of death, there came a look of peace over the Count's face, such as I never have seen on mortal man.

The gypsies, seeing their cargo crumble away to dust, rode away as if for their very lives. We all quickly gathered around our injured friend, but a sad nod from Dr. Seward told me nothing could be done.

"I am only too happy to have been of service!" said the dying Quincey as Mina took his hand. "Oh, God! It was worth for this to die! Look! Look!"

The sun was now right down upon the mountain top, and the red gleams fell upon Mina's face, so that it was bathed in a rosy light. We all fell on our knees and gave thanks. Quincey spoke:

"Now God be thanked that all has not been in vain! See! The snow is not more stainless than her forehead! The curse has passed away." And to her joy, Mina knew that the mark of the Sacred Wafer—the mark of God—had vanished from her.

We watched in bitter grief, for with a smile on his face and in silence, he died, our gallant gentleman.

The curse of Count Dracula was finally, mercifully over.